Contents

*Levels**	*Title*	*Composer*	*Page*
C (T)	Table-Tennis Tango	Derek Hasted	2
C (T)	La Bergamasca	Trad. Italian arr. Christopher Susans	3
C (T)	Steamin' and a-rollin'	Stephen Goss	4
C (T)	Tumbao	David Cottam	5
C (T)	Sunday Morning	Bob Power	6
C C	Squabble	Richard Wright	6
C C	Touch and Go	Stephen Kenyon	7
C C	Ground and Round	Richard Wright	7
C B	April Shower	Debbie Cracknell	8
C B	Russian Lament	Stephen Goss	9
C C (T)	Lonesome Trail	Debbie Cracknell and Cornelius Bruinsma	10
C C (T)	Yee-ha	Cornelius Bruinsma	11
C C C	Wintersong	David Harvey	12
C C (B)	Coronach	Fran Gray	13
C B B	Warriors	Richard Wright	14
C B (B)	Jammin' in the Traffic Jam	Derek Hasted	15

*C = copper; B = bronze; T = teacher; ( ) = the line must be played but cannot be assessed for a Medal.

Table-Tennis Tango

Derek Hasted

Like a ping-pong sing-song ♩ = *c.*108

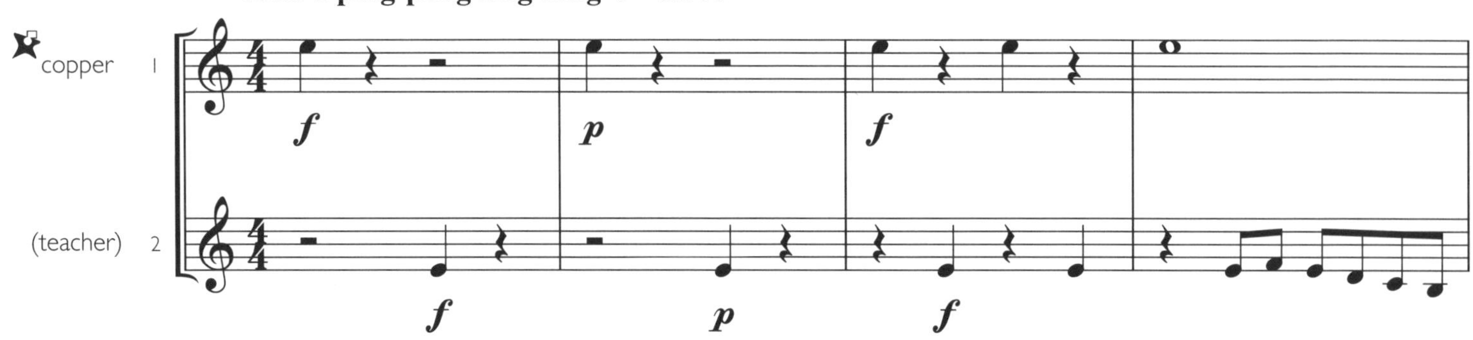

La Bergamasca

Trad. Italian arr. Christopher Susans

Steamin' and a-rollin'

Stephen Goss

Tumbao

David Cottam

Sunday Morning

Bob Power

Squabble

Richard Wright

⦹ = Snap pizzicato: pull the string away from the fingerboard, between thumb and index finger, then let go so it snaps back.

Touch and Go

Stephen Kenyon

Ground and Round

Richard Wright

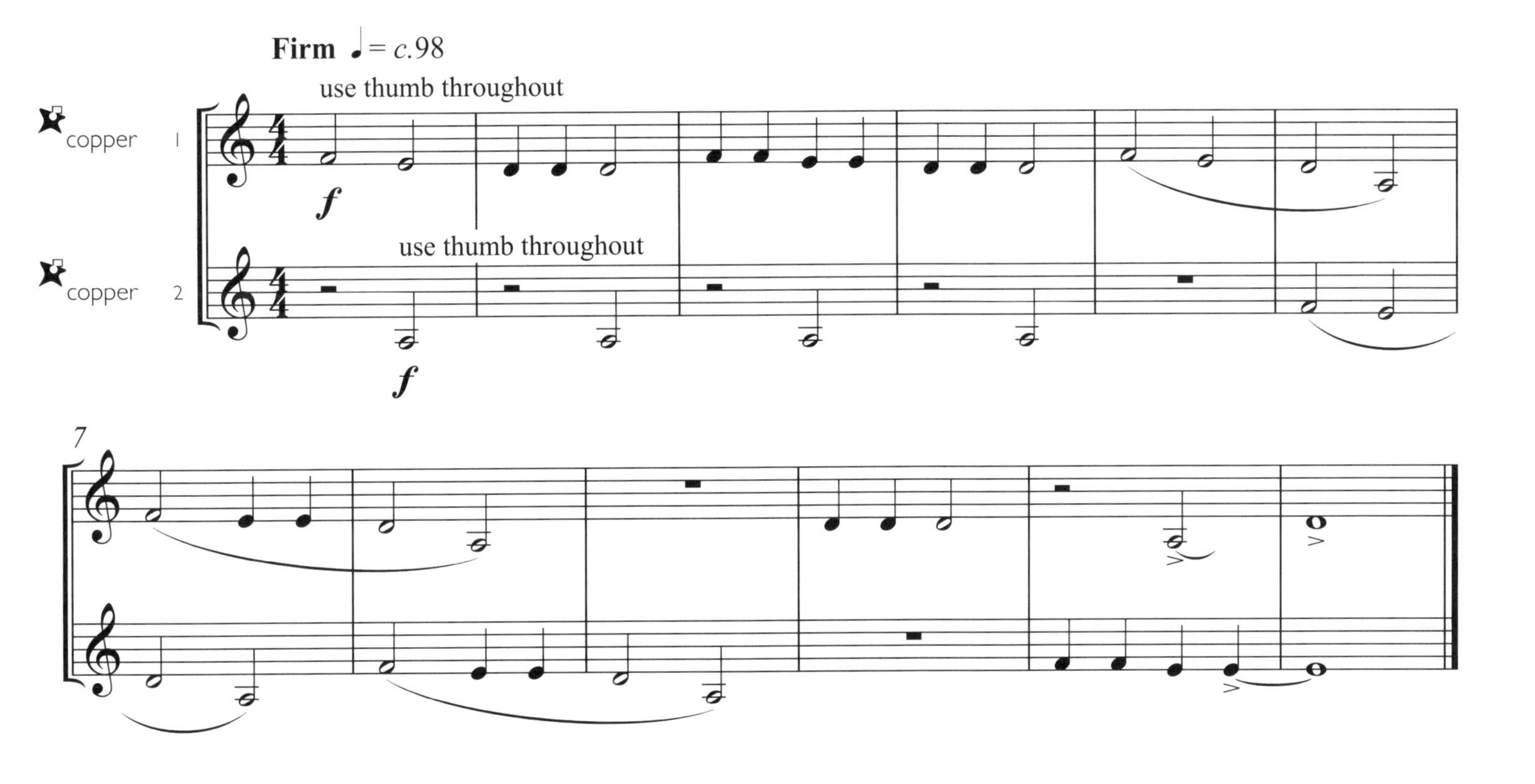

April Shower

Debbie Cracknell

Russian Lament

Stephen Goss

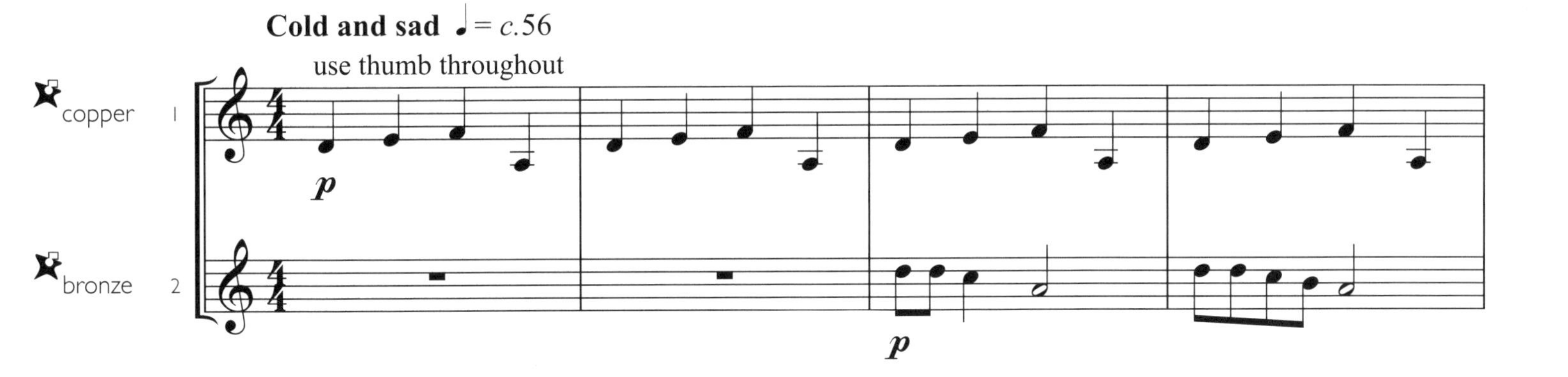

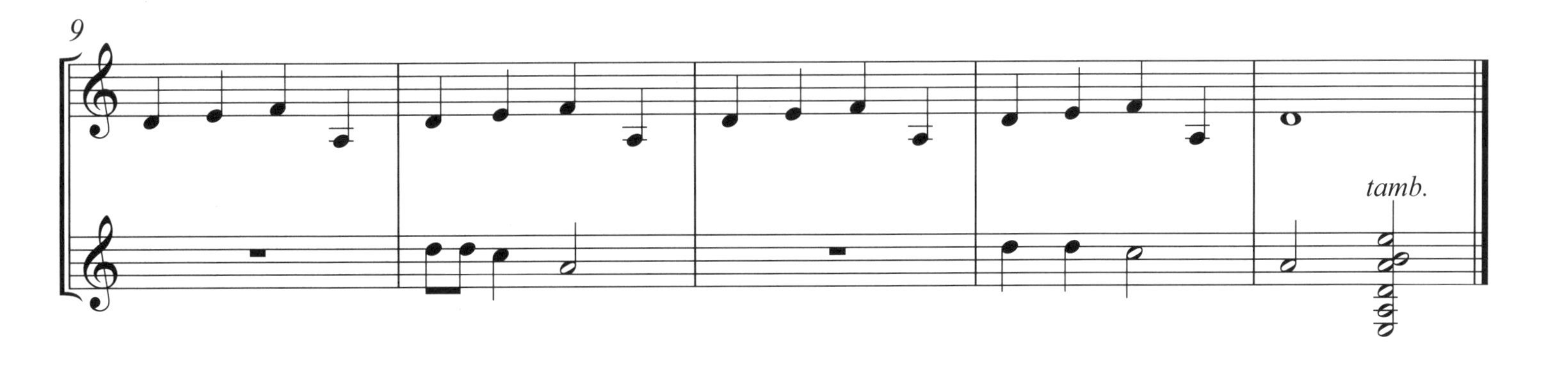

Lonesome Trail

Debbie Cracknell and Cornelius Bruinsma

= Tap guitar either side of the strings, with thumb on beats one and three, and fingers on beats two and four.

Yee-ha

Cornelius Bruinsma

Wintersong

David Harvey

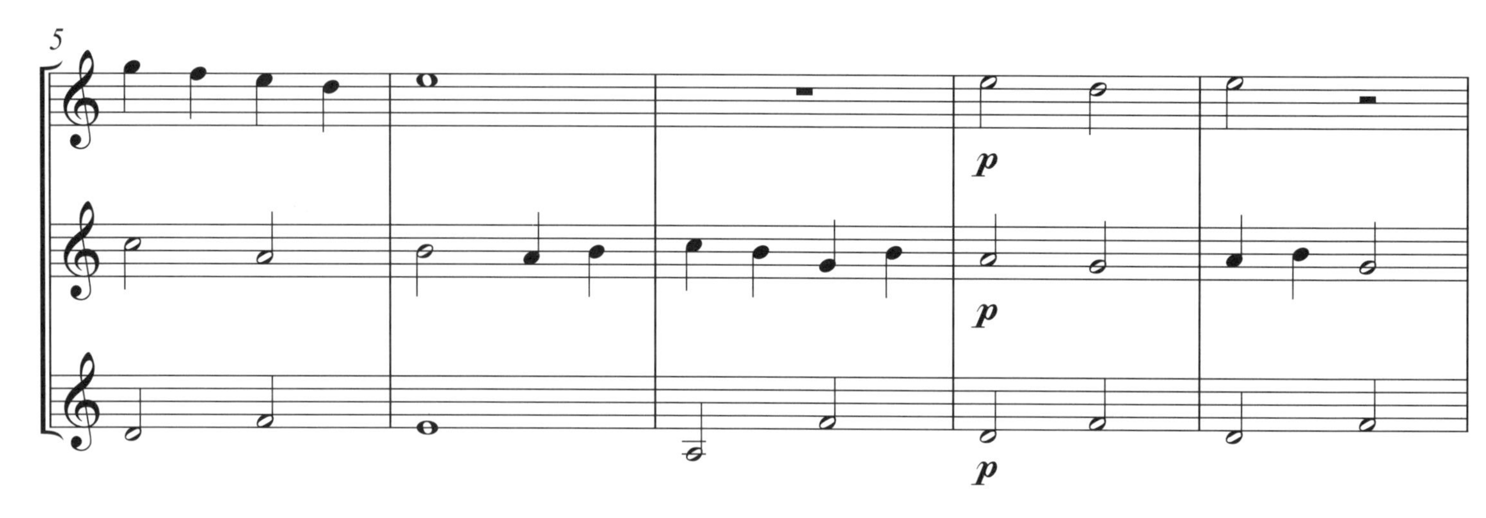

Coronach

Fran Gray

Warriors

Richard Wright

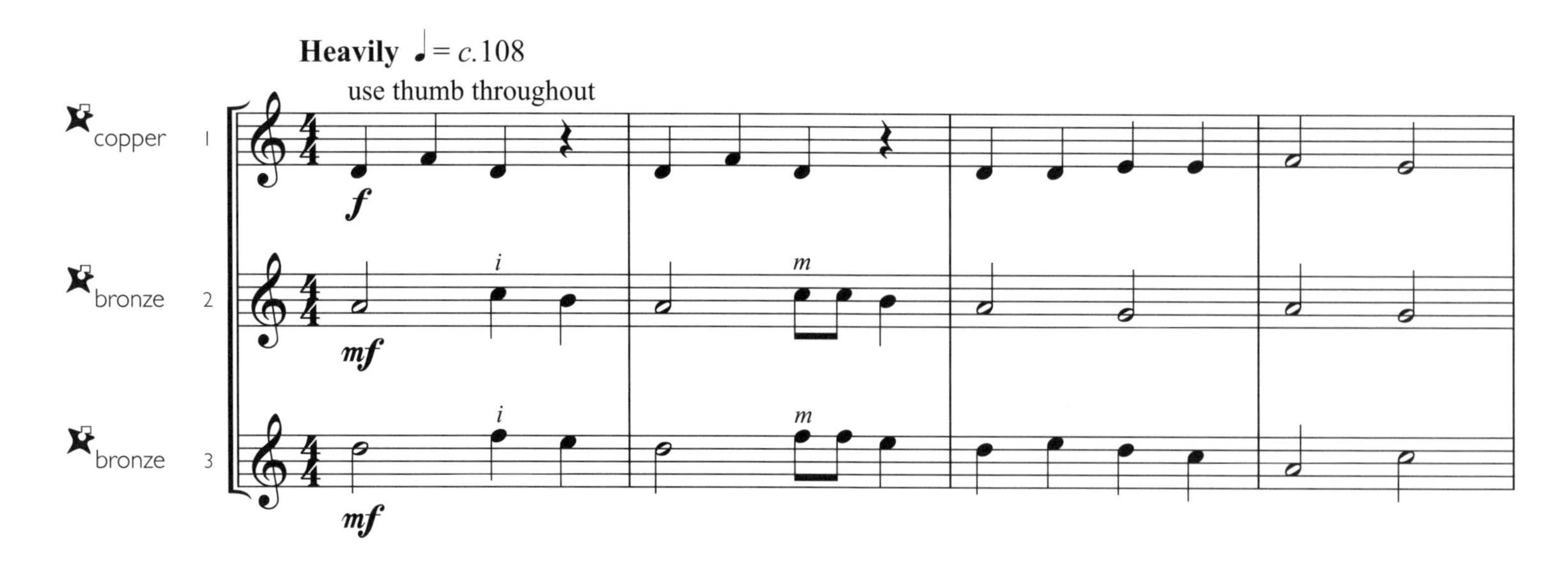

Jammin' in the Traffic Jam

Derek Hasted